SURPRISES

William K. Durr
Jean M. LePere
Mary Lou Alsin

CONSULTANT: Paul McKee

HOUGHTON MIFFLIN COMPANY · Boston

Atlanta · Dallas · Geneva, Illinois · Hopewell, New Jersey · Palo Alto · Toronto

Illustrated by: JAN PALMER

ROBERT JACKSON · TAD KRUMEICH

1978 IMPRESSION
Copyright © 1976, by Houghton Mifflin Company

Printed in the U.S.A.
ISBN: 0-395-20404-6

Contents

Bob   Jan

Ricky   Sam   Carla

Carla Wants to Fish

 Here is the school bus!
Come on, Carla.

 I'm not going to school.

 You have to go.

 I'm going to get a fish.
And I can't fish in school.

 Where is Carla?

 Carla isn't going to school.

 Is she sick?

 Carla isn't sick.

She wants to go fishing.

Carla! Get on the bus!
You have to go to school.

I want to go fishing.
And I can't fish in school.

This is a school day, Carla.

I'm not going today.
I have to go fishing.

Carla, where are you going?

This is a school day.

 I'm not going to school today.

I want to play.

I'm going to fish here in the park.

9

You can't go fishing on a school day.

You have to go to school.

 I can't go to school.

I take the bus to school.

I'm going to play in the park.

And I'm going to have fun.

Fishing and playing are fun.

School isn't fun.

This is no fun.

I can't play with Jan.

She is in school.

And I can't play with Bob.

He is in school with Jan.

 Is it fun to play in the park, Carla?

 No. It's not fun.

I can't go fishing.

And I can't play with Jan and Bob.

I want to go to school.

Will you take me there?

 Bob! Jan! Here I am.

I can't go fishing on a school day.

 You can go fishing there, Carla.

 This is a funny day.

I can't fish in the park.

And I can fish in school.

I Can't Smile

I can't go to school.

Today is picture day.

And I can't smile.

Come here and look.

 Jan, you have a nice smile.

 No, the picture will not look nice.
I have no teeth.

 You look nice, Jan.
You have to go to school.
Carla is here.

 Today is picture day, Jan.

We are going to have fun.

 It isn't fun for me.

I can't smile for my picture.

My teeth have not come in.

And I look funny.

 You will not look funny.

 I'll see you in school, Carla.

I have to go in here.

 I'll come with you.

 No, you go on.

 Mrs. Day can take my picture.

I'll look nice now.

I can smile!

 Mrs. Day is here, Jan.

She is going to take the pictures now.

 Look here and smile!
This will be a nice picture, Carla.

 Will Jan's picture be nice, Mrs. Day?
Jan can't smile today.

 I can smile now, Carla.
I will look nice for the picture.

 You have funny teeth, Jan.
This is going to be a funny picture.

 I want a nice picture.

 A nice picture can't have funny teeth.

 Here are the funny teeth, Mrs. Day.

 You'll have a nice picture now, Jan.

 Your pictures are here.

You can have your pictures now.

 I want to see your picture, Jan.

Where is it?

 Here it is.

Jan, you look funny in this picture.

 I look nice, Carla.

The teeth look funny.

 Here I am with no teeth.

 You look nice with no teeth, Jan.

 This is a nice picture.
And I have a nice smile in it.

Sam's Big Fish

 Can you take me to get a fish, Mom?

I want to take it to school.

 You can't take a fish to school.

 I have to have a fish.

It's Fish Day, Mom.

 Will it have to be a real fish?

 We can't have a real fish here, Sam.

Your cat will get it.

Can you take a fish picture to school?

I have a nice fish picture for you.

I don't want to take a fish picture.

Bob and Jan and Ricky and Carla have fish.

I want a fish to take to school.

Fish Day will be no fun for me!

 You don't have to take a fish picture.

You will have a fish.

I'll help you get one.

You'll have one for Fish Day, Sam.

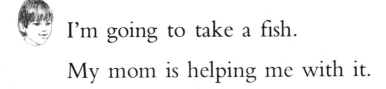 I have a fish for Fish Day.

Is your fish real?

It's real.

You can't look at it now.

You can look at it on Fish Day.

What are you going to take to school?

I'm going to take a fish.

My mom is helping me with it.

 Your cat will get the fish.

 The cat will not get this fish.

My fish will scare the cat.

 What fish can scare a cat?

 This one can.

You'll see it on Fish Day, Bob.

 Sam's fish can scare cats.

 What a fish!
Is it big, Sam?

 It's this big.
And it can fly!

 Fly! Fish can't fly, Sam.

 This one can.

This is my fish.

And it's real.

It can scare big fish.

That is a nice fish, Bob.

Can we see your fish, Jan?

35

Here is my fish.
It's not a real one.
Look out, Bob.
It will get you.

Bob's fish can scare big fish.
And Jan's fish can scare Bob!
Isn't that funny?

We want to see Sam's flying fish!

Where is it, Sam?

 Here it is!

It can't fly in school.

 Sam, that is not a fish.

What is it?

It can't fly.

Can it?

Sam, it is a fish!

And it can fly.
Look at it go.

It's fun to be out here, Sam.
And see a fish that can fly!

Mom and the Cat   Mom's Picture

No Lions and Tigers

Lion, will you come out here?

I want to take your picture.

Can't you see that I'm sick?

You can't take my picture now, Frog.

I'm a sick lion.

And I can't smile.

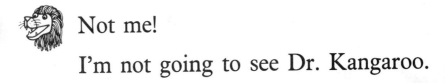You will have to go and see Kangaroo.

She is the one that can help you.

Not me!

I'm not going to see Dr. Kangaroo.

 What will she do to me?

 Dr. Kangaroo will look at your teeth.
And she will help you.
Don't you want to get help?

 I do want help for my teeth.
It's no fun to be sick.
I'm scared to go to Dr. Kangaroo.

 Lion is here, Dr. Kangaroo.

And he wants to see you.

What is Lion here for?

He is sick.

Can you take a look at Lion's teeth?

I don't work on big teeth.

And I don't work on lions and tigers.

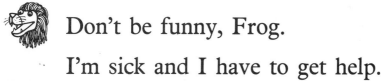 Dr. Kangaroo is scared of big teeth.
And you are scared of Dr. Kangaroo.

Don't be funny, Frog.
I'm sick and I have to get help.

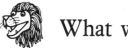 Dr. Kangaroo will not work on lions.

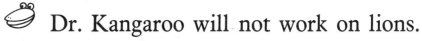 What will I do now, Frog?

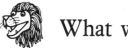 You can go to Dr. Kangaroo.
You will not be a lion.

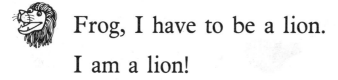 Frog, I have to be a lion.
I am a lion!

There, Lion.

This looks nice on you.

Now you are a big rabbit.

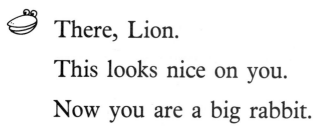 Will Dr. Kangaroo work on a rabbit?

She will work on your teeth, Lion.

Now that you are a rabbit!

 Dr. Kangaroo, a rabbit is here.

He wants to see you.

What a big rabbit you are!

I'll help you, Rabbit.

Come in! Come in!

My, you have big teeth for a rabbit.

I can see the sick teeth.

 Did you take my teeth out?

 I did not take your teeth out, Rabbit.

Look in here.

You'll see that your teeth look nice.

49

 My teeth do look nice now!
And I'm not sick, Frog.
See what a nice smile I have.

 That is a nice smile!

 It's not a rabbit smile.
And you are not a rabbit!

 I'm a lion.

And you don't work on lions.

I did have to get help.

 You can come and see me, Lion.

And you will not have to be a rabbit.

Your big teeth don't scare me.

You are a funny lion!

Fun With a LION

 Do you want to play with me, Ricky?

I'm going to the jungle.

See the lion in this picture?

I'm going to play with it.

 Where is this jungle?

 Come on, Ricky.

I'll take you there.

I'm not going to play with a real lion.

Real lions scare me.

 It's not a real lion.

We're going to have fun playing jungle.

 Where did the lion go?

It's not real.

And it can't run.

 Real lions can run, Bob.

 The lion isn't real.

It can't run away.

How can a play lion get away?

The lion isn't out there.

Did it run away?

 The lion will not be out there now.

 Where will it be?

We want to play with it.

 That will be a surprise for you.

The lion is on a truck now.

You'll have to go and find it.

 We are looking for a lion.

And it's on a truck.

 Did you see a lion on a truck?

 No, I did not see a lion on a truck.

I did see one at the zoo.

 Real lions are at the zoo.

 This one isn't real, Ricky.

We're not looking for a real lion.

It's a play lion.

We're playing that we're in the jungle.

And we can't play without that lion.

How can we find it?

I did see a lion in there.

Go in and look for it.

 We are looking for a lion.

Do you have one here?

 We have one here.

I'll take you to see it.

It's in there.

That is a real lion!

 It looks real.

 It's not the lion we want.

 It's on a truck.

And we can't find the truck.

 We're playing that we're in the jungle.

And we have to have that lion.

Can you help?

LIONS

 I'll find out where that lion is going.

 I have a nice surprise for you.

You will have to go to the park.

That is where you will find the lion.

Here we are in the park.

I don't see the truck, do you?

 No, I don't see it.

And I don't see the lion.

It's not here.

There it is, Ricky.

That is the lion we want.

This is a nice surprise for me.

The lion isn't real.

Come on, Ricky.

We can play jungle now.